Addition Facts in Seven Days

by Dr. Carl H. Seltzer

+	0	1	2	3	4	5	6	7	8	9
0	0	1	2	3	4	5	6	7	8	9
1	1	2	3	4	5	6	7	8	9	10
2	2	3	4	5	6	7	8	9	10	11
3	3	4	5	6	7	8	9	10	11	12
4	4	5	6	7	8	9	10	11	12	13
5	5	6	7	8	9	10	11	12	13	14
6	6	7	8	9	10	11	12	13	14	15
7	7	8	9	10	11	12	13	14	15	16
8	8	9	10	11	12	13	14	15	16	17
9	9	10	11	12	13	14	15	16	17	18

Day 2, Memorize:

$2 + 6 = 8$

$4 + 4 = 8$

$3 + 6 = 9$

$3 + 5 = 8$

$2 + 7 = 9$

$4 + 5 = 9$

Send ***Letter B*** home to parents and review Day 1.

2. $2 + 3 =$ ☐

3. $2 + 4 =$ ☐

4. $2 + 5 =$ ☐

5. $3 + 3 =$ ☐

6. $3 + 4 =$ ☐

7. $2 + 6 =$ ☐

8. $3 + 5 =$ ☐

9. $4 + 4 =$ ☐

10. $2 + 7 =$ ☐

11. $3 + 6 =$ ☐

Didax Educational Resources
www.didax.com

Printed in the United States of America.

This book is printed on recycled paper.

Order Number 2-5292
ISBN 978-1-58324-274-2

C D E F G 14 13 12 11 10

395 Main Street
Rowley, MA 01969
www.didax.com

Addition Facts in Seven Days

Foreword

Students need certain facts at their disposal when doing mathematics, such as the addition facts to 20 and multiplication facts. Research shows that children's instant recall of these basic number facts will only progress from short-term memory (easily forgotten) to the long-term memory through constant practice and reinforcement.

Addition Facts in Seven Days offers an easy-to-follow systematic program to promote the learning of these essential number facts. Easily incorporated into any weekly program, teachers introduce the facts, which are then reinforced at home. Letters to parents are included in the book, which clearly state the facts to be practiced that day.

Strategies are included to help reduce the number of facts to be learned. Students will be happy to know that only thirty-six facts need to be memorized to master addition!

Addition Facts in Seven Days is an ideal mathematics support program, which allows students to achieve instant recall and understanding of number facts. Students will enjoy challenging both themselves and each other, as they work towards learning the set of number facts for each day.

Contents

This book includes teacher notes, activity sheets, letters to parents and assessment tasks.

Addition Facts in Seven Days

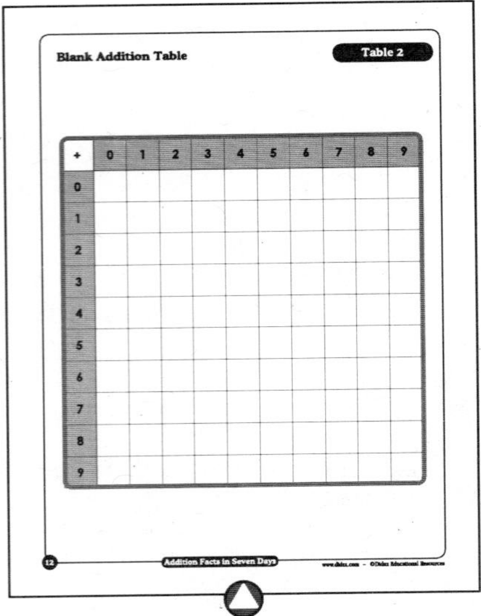

Blank Addition Table

Table 2

+	0	1	2	3	4	5	6	7	8	9
0										
1										
2										
3										
4										
5										
6										
7										
8										
9										

12 Addition Facts in Seven Days www.didax.com ~ ©Didax Educational Resources

Students are introduced to the facts by completing a blank addition table. Patterns and families are discussed.

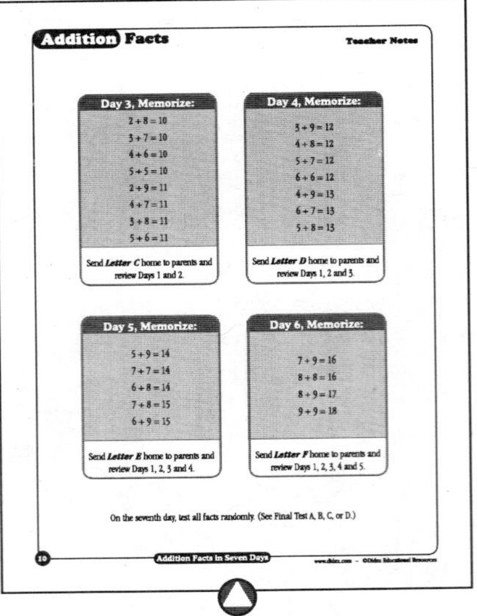

Addition Facts

Teacher Notes

Day 3, Memorize:

2 + 8 = 10
3 + 7 = 10
4 + 6 = 10
5 + 5 = 10
2 + 9 = 11
4 + 7 = 11
3 + 8 = 11
5 + 6 = 11

Send ***Letter C*** home to parents and review Days 1 and 2.

Day 4, Memorize:

3 + 9 = 12
4 + 8 = 12
5 + 7 = 12
6 + 6 = 12
4 + 9 = 13
6 + 7 = 13
5 + 8 = 13

Send ***Letter D*** home to parents and review Days 1, 2 and 3.

Day 5, Memorize:

5 + 9 = 14
7 + 7 = 14
6 + 8 = 14
7 + 8 = 15
6 + 9 = 15

Send ***Letter E*** home to parents and review Days 1, 2, 3 and 4.

Day 6, Memorize:

7 + 9 = 16
8 + 8 = 16
8 + 9 = 17
9 + 9 = 18

Send ***Letter F*** home to parents and review Days 1, 2, 3, 4 and 5.

On the seventh day, test all facts randomly. (See Final Test A, B, C, or D.)

10 Addition Facts in Seven Days www.didax.com ~ ©Didax Educational Resources

Teacher notes clearly state the facts to be introduced and learned each day.

A corresponding letter is sent home with the students. Parents are involved in the practice and reinforcement stage of the program.

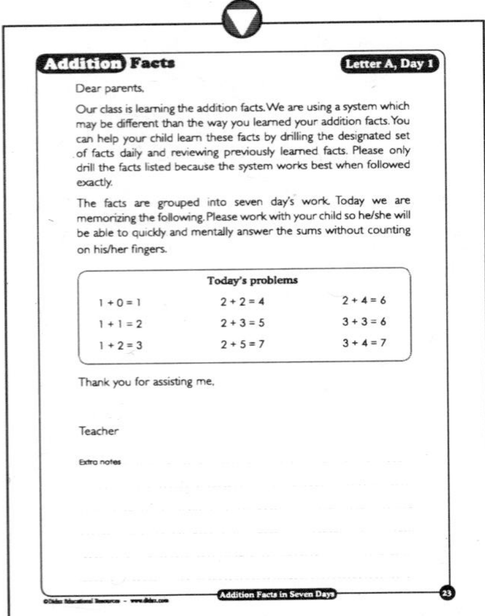

Addition Facts

Letter A, Day 1

Dear parents,

Our class is learning the addition facts. We are using a system which may be different than the way you learned your addition facts. You can help your child learn these facts by drilling the designated set of facts daily and reviewing previously learned facts. Please only drill the facts listed because the system works best when followed exactly.

The facts are grouped into seven day's work. Today we are memorizing the following. Please work with your child so he/she will be able to quickly and mentally answer the sums without counting on his/her fingers.

Today's problems

1 + 0 = 1	2 + 2 = 4	2 + 4 = 6
1 + 1 = 2	2 + 3 = 5	3 + 3 = 6
1 + 2 = 3	2 + 5 = 7	3 + 4 = 7

Thank you for assisting me,

Teacher

Extra notes

©Didax Educational Resources ~ www.didax.com Addition Facts in Seven Days 23

Students are tested the following day on newly learned facts. Previously learned facts are also included and reviewed in the test.

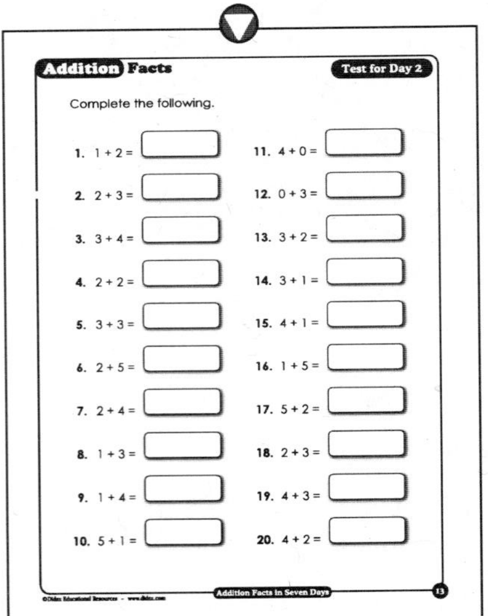

Addition Facts

Test for Day 2

Complete the following.

1. 1 + 2 =
2. 2 + 3 =
3. 3 + 4 =
4. 2 + 2 =
5. 3 + 3 =
6. 2 + 5 =
7. 2 + 4 =
8. 1 + 3 =
9. 1 + 4 =
10. 5 + 1 =
11. 4 + 0 =
12. 0 + 3 =
13. 3 + 2 =
14. 3 + 1 =
15. 4 + 1 =
16. 1 + 5 =
17. 5 + 2 =
18. 2 + 3 =
19. 4 + 3 =
20. 4 + 2 =

©Didax Educational Resources ~ www.didax.com Addition Facts in Seven Days 13

Teacher Notes

Facts and Algorithms

One of the most important skills students need is a mastery of the basic computational skills.

All people require the ability to mentally compute basic addition and multiplication facts quickly and accurately. It is also very important for students to understand all they can about addition and multiplication and how they relate. Students should use manipulatives to help them reinforce their understanding of the concepts.

This book does not purposely mean to address the use of manipulatives, but students need to experience the concepts involved prior to memorizing facts.

Firstly, I would like to distinguish between a fact and an algorithm.

A ***fact*** *is a piece of information that is accepted as true. In mathematics there are many facts that students are required to learn. Hopefully they will already have some understanding of the facts and what they mean. In mathematics, facts are usually memorized. Some examples of math facts are addition facts, multiplication facts and definitions.*

An ***algorithm*** *is a systematic method to solve a problem … a rule. While algorithms use facts, there is a difference between the two.*

Let us look at some examples:

Facts: 2 + 3 = 5, 4 + 8 = 12, etc.

Problem:

$$\begin{array}{r} 24 \\ +\ 38 \\ \hline \end{array}$$

Students are taught to solve this problem by adding 8 + 4 = 12 (a fact). Then, to add 2 + 3 (really 20 + 30) and get 5 (really 50). 2 + 3 = 5 is a fact. Then 12 + 50 = 2 + 0 (a fact) and 1 + 5 = 6 (a fact), to get 62.

It is also a fact that 12 is equal to 10 + 2 and 50 is equal to 5(10) + 0. But the procedure used in solving this problem is the algorithm. One can see from this example that all addition facts and all multiplication facts are single digits less than ten.

9 × 12 = 108 is an algorithm involving the facts 9 × 2 and 9 × 1 (the 1 being in 10s place), yielding 18 + 90 = 108.

Therefore, it is never necessary to memorize 12 × 13, etc., because this product is produced by an algorithm.

It is helpful for students to complete a blank addition or mulitplication table themselves, providing them with a better understanding of how to read these tables.

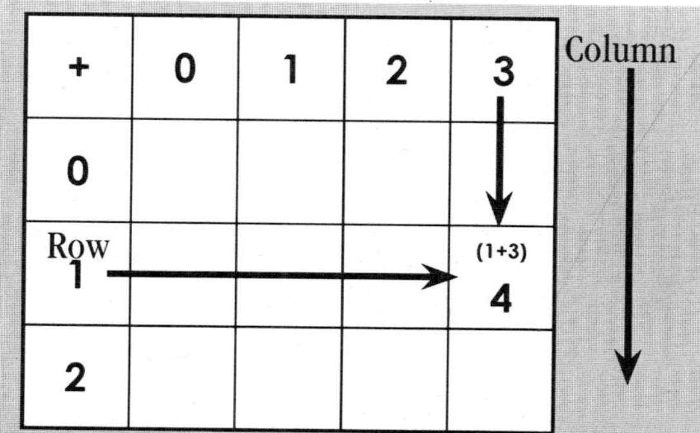

Students can use any method they wish to complete the table, but you may need to point out that where a column and a row intersect is where the sum or product is placed.

Younger students may use manipulatives such as Unifix® cubes, or counting on their fingers to find the sums.

Older students may also use manipulatives or arrays to find sums or products. For example, an array of dots that is 3×5 would contain 15 dots.

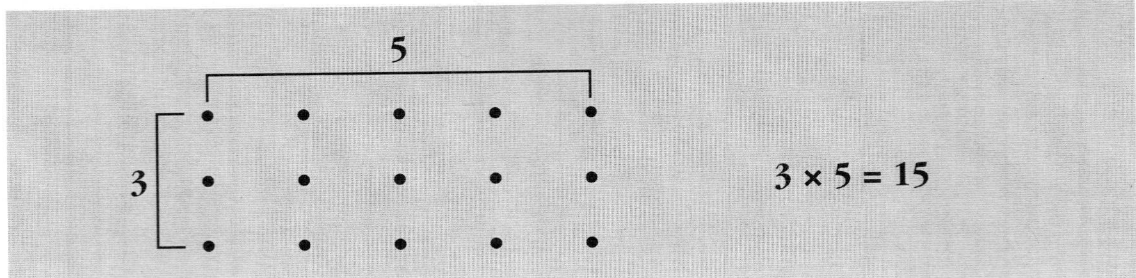

Students experiment with manipulatives when finding sums. Finding "families" of facts equal to a specific number is a great way to complete a blank addition table (Table 2, page 12) and also helps students understand how this system works.

Suppose we use two different colors of Unifix® cubes and make sets equal to 6.

We could get:

1 red + 5 yellow (6 cubes)

2 red + 4 yellow (6 cubes)

3 red + 3 yellow (6 cubes)

4 red + 2 yellow (6 cubes)

5 red + 1 yellow (6 cubes)

Regardless of how we do it, they all produce a total of 6. While 1 red and 5 yellow is different than 5 red and 1 yellow, each produces a total of 6 cubes. Therefore, it is clear that if we are only interested in the sum of the two sets, then $1 + 5 = 5 + 1 = 6$, etc.

After students have completed their own addition tables, give them Table 1 (page 11) and have them check their work. Follow this by asking students to examine their tables and look for patterns.

List all the patterns the students can find and discuss them with the class. The students may not discover the following patterns, so you may need to point them out.

Circle all sums of 1 and record:

$$1 + 0 = 0 + 1$$

Circle all sums of 2 and record:

$$2 = 0 + 2 = 1 + 1 = 2 + 0$$

Circle all sums of 3 and record:

$$3 = 0 + 3 = 1 + 2 = 2 + 1 = 3 + 0$$

Circle all sums of 4 and record:

$$4 = 0 + 4 = 1 + 3 = 2 + 2 = 3 + 1 = 4 + 0$$

Circle all sums of 5 and record:

$$5 = 0 + 5 = 1 + 4 = 2 + 3 = 3 + 2 = 4 + 1 = 5 + 0$$

Circle all sums of 6 and record:

$$6 = 0 + 6 = 1 + 5 = 2 + 4 = 3 + 3 = 4 + 2 = 5 + 1 = 6 + 0$$

Circle all sums of 7 and record:

$7 = 0 + 7 = 1 + 6 = 2 + 5 = 3 + 4 = 4 + 3 = 5 + 2 = 6 + 1 = 7 + 0$

Circle all sums of 8 and record:

$8 = 0 + 8 = 1 + 7 = 2 + 6 = 3 + 5 = 4 + 4 = 5 + 3 = 6 + 2 = 7 + 1 = 8 + 0$

Circle all sums of 9 and record:

$9 = 0 + 9 = 1 + 8 = 2 + 7 = 3 + 6 = 4 + 5 = 5 + 4 = 6 + 3 = 7 + 2 = 8 + 1 = 9 + 0$

Circle all sums of 10 and record:

$10 = 1 + 9 = 2 + 8 = 3 + 7 = 4 + 6 = 5 + 5 = 6 + 4 = 7 + 3 = 8 + 2 = 9 + 1$

Circle all sums of 11 and record:

$11 = 2 + 9 = 3 + 8 = 4 + 7 = 5 + 6 = 6 + 5 = 7 + 4 = 8 + 3 = 9 + 2$

Circle all sums of 12 and record:

$12 = 3 + 9 = 4 + 8 = 5 + 7 = 6 + 6 = 7 + 5 = 8 + 4 = 9 + 3$

Circle all sums of 13 and record:

$13 = 4 + 9 = 5 + 8 = 6 + 7 = 7 + 6 = 8 + 5 = 9 + 4$

Circle all sums of 14 and record:

$14 = 5 + 9 = 6 + 8 = 7 + 7 = 8 + 6 = 9 + 5$

Circle all sums of 15 and record:

$15 = 6 + 9 = 7 + 8 = 8 + 7 = 9 + 6$

Circle all sums of 16 and record:

$16 = 7 + 9 = 8 + 8 = 9 + 7$

Circle all sums of 17 and record:

$17 = 8 + 9 = 9 + 8$

Circle all sums of 18 and record:

$18 = 9 + 9$

Looking at the sentences we recorded, it is obvious that there are a number of **facts** that are the same *except* for their order. For example, $3 + 4 = 4 + 3$, and once we know one **fact** we know both.

This is called the **Commutative Principle of Addition**, and reduces the actual number of **facts** we need to memorize from 100 to 36 because we do not need to memorize $a + 0 = a$, nor adding 1, just the next counting number.

Furthermore, since any number + 0 equals that number ($9 + 0 = 9$), and any number plus one equals the next counting number, we don't really need to memorize those sums either. This cuts the total amount of memorized addition facts to 36.

This means that the number of facts necessary to memorize are limited to the following "families":

4 = 2 + 2
5 = 2 + 3
6 = 2 + 4 = 3 + 3
7 = 2 + 5 = 3 + 4
8 = 2 + 6 = 3 + 5 = 4 + 4
9 = 2 + 7 = 3 + 6 = 4 + 5
10 = 2 + 8 = 3 + 7 = 4 + 6 = 5 + 5
11 = 2 + 9 = 3 + 8 = 4 + 7 = 5 + 6
12 = 3 + 9 = 4 + 8 = 5 + 7 = 6 + 6
13 = 4 + 9 = 5 + 8 = 6 + 7
14 = 5 + 9 = 6 + 8 = 7 + 7
15 = 6 + 9 = 7 + 8
16 = 7 + 9 = 8 + 8
17 = 8 + 9
18 = 9 + 9

To make the memorization process more organized, the following seven-day plan is suggested:

Day 1, Memorize:

2 + 2 = 4
2 + 3 = 5
2 + 4 = 6
3 + 3 = 6
2 + 5 = 7
3 + 4 = 7

Send ***Letter A*** home to parents.

Day 2, Memorize:

2 + 6 = 8
4 + 4 = 8
3 + 5 = 8
3 + 6 = 9
2 + 7 = 9
4 + 5 = 9

Send ***Letter B*** home to parents and review Day 1.

Day 3, Memorize:

$2 + 8 = 10$

$3 + 7 = 10$

$4 + 6 = 10$

$5 + 5 = 10$

$2 + 9 = 11$

$4 + 7 = 11$

$3 + 8 = 11$

$5 + 6 = 11$

Send ***Letter C*** home to parents and review Days 1 and 2.

Day 4, Memorize:

$3 + 9 = 12$

$4 + 8 = 12$

$5 + 7 = 12$

$6 + 6 = 12$

$4 + 9 = 13$

$6 + 7 = 13$

$5 + 8 = 13$

Send ***Letter D*** home to parents and review Days 1, 2 and 3.

Day 5, Memorize:

$5 + 9 = 14$

$7 + 7 = 14$

$6 + 8 = 14$

$7 + 8 = 15$

$6 + 9 = 15$

Send ***Letter E*** home to parents and review Days 1, 2, 3 and 4.

Day 6, Memorize:

$7 + 9 = 16$

$8 + 8 = 16$

$8 + 9 = 17$

$9 + 9 = 18$

Send ***Letter F*** home to parents and review Days 1, 2, 3, 4 and 5.

On the seventh day, test all facts randomly. (See Final Test A, B, C, or D.)

Addition Table of Facts

Table 1

+	0	1	2	3	4	5	6	7	8	9
0	0	1	2	3	4	5	6	7	8	9
1	1	2	3	4	5	6	7	8	9	10
2	2	3	4	5	6	7	8	9	10	11
3	3	4	5	6	7	8	9	10	11	12
4	4	5	6	7	8	9	10	11	12	13
5	5	6	7	8	9	10	11	12	13	14
6	6	7	8	9	10	11	12	13	14	15
7	7	8	9	10	11	12	13	14	15	16
8	8	9	10	11	12	13	14	15	16	17
9	9	10	11	12	13	14	15	16	17	18

Addition Table of Facts

Table 1

+	0	1	2	3	4	5	6	7	8	9
0	0	1	2	3	4	5	6	7	8	9
1	1	2	3	4	5	6	7	8	9	10
2	2	3	4	5	6	7	8	9	10	11
3	3	4	5	6	7	8	9	10	11	12
4	4	5	6	7	8	9	10	11	12	13
5	5	6	7	8	9	10	11	12	13	14
6	6	7	8	9	10	11	12	13	14	15
7	7	8	9	10	11	12	13	14	15	16
8	8	9	10	11	12	13	14	15	16	17
9	9	10	11	12	13	14	15	16	17	18

Blank Addition Table

Table 2

+	0	1	2	3	4	5	6	7	8	9
0										
1										
2										
3										
4										
5										
6										
7										
8										
9										

Addition Facts

Test for Day 2

Complete the following.

1. 1 + 2 = 3
2. 2 + 3 = 5
3. 3 + 4 = 7
4. 2 + 2 = 4
5. 3 + 3 = 6
6. 2 + 5 = 7
7. 2 + 4 = 6
8. 1 + 3 = 4
9. 1 + 4 = 5
10. 5 + 1 = 6
11. 4 + 0 = 4
12. 0 + 3 = 3
13. 3 + 2 = 5
14. 3 + 1 = 4
15. 4 + 1 = 4
16. 1 + 5 = 6
17. 5 + 2 = 7
18. 2 + 3 = 5
19. 4 + 3 = 7
20. 4 + 2 = 6

Complete the following.

1. 4 + 5 = 9
2. 2 + 2 = 4
3. 2 + 5 = 7
4. 2 + 7 = 9
5. 2 + 3 = 5
6. 1 + 8 = 9
7. 3 + 5 = 8
8. 3 + 6 = 9
9. 2 + 4 = 6
10. 5 + 3 = 8
11. 7 + 2 = 9
12. 6 + 2 = 8
13. 5 + 4 = 9
14. 3 + 6 = 9
15. 6 + 1 = 7
16. 7 + 2 = 9
17. 8 + 0 = 8
18. 4 + 4 = 8
19. 3 + 3 = 6
20. 6 + 3 = 9
21. 2 + 6 = 8
22. 4 + 5 = 9
23. 2 + 3 = 5
24. 2 + 7 = 9

Addition Facts

Test for Day 4

Complete the following.

1. 5 + 5 = 10
2. 2 + 6 = 8
3. 4 + 6 = 10
4. 4 + 4 = 8
5. 3 + 7 = 10
6. 2 + 7 = 9
7. 4 + 2 = 6
8. 4 + 3 = 7
9. 5 + 6 = 11
10. 5 + 2 = 7
11. 8 + 2 = 10
12. 9 + 2 = 11
13. 3 + 6 =
14. 2 + 3 =
15. 8 + 3 =
16. 2 + 9 =
17. 3 + 5 =
18. 7 + 3 =
19. 3 + 8 =
20. 4 + 5 =
21. 4 + 7 =
22. 4 + 2 =
23. 3 + 3 =
24. 5 + 5 =

Addition Facts

Test for Day 5

Complete the following.

1. 3 + 5 =
2. 3 + 7 =
3. 5 + 7 =
4. 6 + 4 =
5. 4 + 9 =
6. 6 + 7 =
7. 9 + 2 =
8. 7 + 2 =
9. 6 + 5 =
10. 7 + 5 =
11. 6 + 3 =
12. 8 + 5 =
13. 4 + 4 =
14. 4 + 8 =
15. 9 + 2 =
16. 6 + 6 =
17. 3 + 8 =
18. 5 + 8 =
19. 4 + 7 =
20. 5 + 3 =
21. 7 + 6 =
22. 4 + 7 =
23. 9 + 4 =
24. 9 + 3 =
25. 5 + 4 =
26. 3 + 3 =

Addition Facts

Test for Day 6

Complete the following.

1. 6 + 9 =
2. 9 + 5 =
3. 4 + 9 =
4. 9 + 2 =
5. 8 + 7 =
6. 9 + 3 =
7. 8 + 3 =
8. 7 + 8 =
9. 7 + 5 =
10. 5 + 5 =
11. 5 + 9 =
12. 4 + 4 =
13. 6 + 7 =
14. 7 + 3 =
15. 3 + 5 =
16. 7 + 2 =
17. 9 + 5 =
18. 5 + 2 =
19. 5 + 8 =
20. 6 + 8 =
21. 4 + 4 =
22. 8 + 6 =
23. 6 + 9 =
24. 7 + 7 =
25. 6 + 3 =
26. 8 + 7 =
27. 8 + 5 =
28. 8 + 4 =
29. 7 + 3 =
30. 6 + 8 =
31. 6 + 5 =
32. 9 + 5 =
33. 6 + 6 =
34. 8 + 4 =
35. 6 + 4 =
36. 9 + 6 =
37. 2 + 6 =
38. 9 + 2 =
39. 6 + 9 =
40. 3 + 3 =

Addition Facts

Test for Day 7

Complete the following.

1. 9 + 9 =
2. 7 + 8 =
3. 2 + 6 =
4. 6 + 7 =
5. 2 + 9 =
6. 4 + 4 =
7. 6 + 9 =
8. 8 + 7 =
9. 4 + 9 =
10. 7 + 7 =
11. 3 + 6 =
12. 2 + 5 =
13. 8 + 8 =
14. 4 + 7 =
15. 5 + 7 =
16. 9 + 5 =
17. 8 + 6 =
18. 9 + 3 =
19. 9 + 7 =
20. 5 + 8 =
21. 2 + 8 =
22. 6 + 7 =
23. 3 + 3 =
24. 9 + 5 =
25. 7 + 5 =
26. 6 + 7 =
27. 7 + 3 =
28. 7 + 9 =
29. 5 + 5 =
30. 5 + 3 =
31. 8 + 5 =
32. 8 + 7 =
33. 7 + 2 =
34. 8 + 6 =
35. 8 + 3 =
36. 9 + 6 =
37. 8 + 4 =
38. 6 + 6 =
39. 7 + 6 =
40. 8 + 9 =
41. 8 + 7 =
42. 8 + 4 =
43. 9 + 3 =
44. 6 + 5 =
45. 6 + 9 =
46. 9 + 8 =
47. 7 + 5 =
48. 9 + 9 =
49. 5 + 4 =
50. 9 + 4 =

Addition Facts

Final Test A

Complete the following.

1. 2 + 2 =
2. 2 + 3 =
3. 2 + 4 =
4. 2 + 5 =
5. 3 + 3 =
6. 3 + 4 =
7. 2 + 6 =
8. 3 + 5 =
9. 4 + 4 =
10. 2 + 7 =
11. 3 + 6 =
12. 4 + 5 =
13. 2 + 8 =
14. 3 + 7 =
15. 4 + 6 =
16. 5 + 5 =
17. 2 + 9 =
18. 3 + 8 =
19. 4 + 7 =
20. 5 + 6 =
21. 3 + 9 =
22. 4 + 8 =
23. 5 + 7 =
24. 6 + 6 =
25. 4 + 9 =
26. 5 + 8 =
27. 6 + 7 =
28. 5 + 9 =
29. 6 + 8 =
30. 7 + 7 =
31. 6 + 9 =
32. 7 + 8 =
33. 7 + 9 =
34. 8 + 8 =
35. 8 + 9 =
36. 9 + 9 =

Addition Facts

Final Test B

Complete the following.

1. 3 + 2 =
2. 4 + 2 =
3. 2 + 2 =
4. 5 + 2 =
5. 3 + 3 =
6. 4 + 3 =
7. 6 + 2 =
8. 5 + 3 =
9. 4 + 4 =
10. 7 + 2 =
11. 6 + 3 =
12. 5 + 4 =
13. 8 + 2 =
14. 7 + 3 =
15. 6 + 4 =
16. 5 + 5 =
17. 9 + 2 =
18. 8 + 3 =
19. 7 + 4 =
20. 6 + 5 =
21. 9 + 3 =
22. 8 + 4 =
23. 7 + 5 =
24. 6 + 6 =
25. 9 + 4 =
26. 8 + 5 =
27. 7 + 6 =
28. 9 + 5 =
29. 8 + 6 =
30. 7 + 7 =
31. 9 + 6 =
32. 8 + 7 =
33. 9 + 7 =
34. 8 + 8 =
35. 9 + 8 =
36. 9 + 9 =

Addition Facts

Final Test C

Complete the following.

1. 2 + 3 =
2. 7 + 6 =
3. 7 + 3 =
4. 9 + 4 =
5. 2 + 4 =
6. 6 + 9 =
7. 7 + 4 =
8. 8 + 6 =
9. 9 + 8 =
10. 3 + 3 =
11. 3 + 5 =
12. 5 + 5 =
13. 3 + 9 =
14. 4 + 4 =
15. 8 + 7 =
16. 2 + 9 =
17. 2 + 2 =
18. 5 + 8 =
19. 2 + 5 =
20. 3 + 4 =
21. 7 + 9 =
22. 5 + 6 =
23. 4 + 6 =
24. 9 + 9 =
25. 2 + 6 =
26. 8 + 4 =
27. 8 + 8 =
28. 9 + 5 =
29. 6 + 6 =
30. 2 + 7 =
31. 7 + 7 =
32. 3 + 8 =
33. 6 + 5 =
34. 2 + 8 =
35. 9 + 6 =
36. 5 + 7 =

Addition Facts

Final Test D

Complete the following.

1. 2 + 2 =
2. 6 + 3 =
3. 2 + 7 =
4. 3 + 4 =
5. 1 + 8 =
6. 4 + 4 =
7. 9 + 2 =
8. 5 + 2 =
9. 4 + 7 =
10. 2 + 1 =
11. 6 + 6 =
12. 4 + 5 =
13. 3 + 7 =
14. 3 + 2 =
15. 6 + 5 =
16. 1 + 4 =
17. 5 + 8 =
18. 2 + 8 =
19. 8 + 6 =
20. 1 + 6 =
21. 6 + 9 =
22. 8 + 7 =
23. 3 + 3 =
24. 5 + 7 =
25. 9 + 7 =
26. 9 + 4 =
27. 7 + 2 =
28. 4 + 6 =
29. 7 + 3 =
30. 2 + 6 =
31. 3 + 9 =
32. 5 + 5 =
33. 3 + 8 =
34. 4 + 2 =
35. 9 + 5 =
36. 7 + 6 =
37. 8 + 8 =
38. 3 + 5 =
39. 3 + 1 =
40. 4 + 8 =
41. 2 + 4 =
42. 7 + 7 =
43. 5 + 1 =
44. 6 + 7 =
45. 7 + 8 =
46. 8 + 9 =
47. 9 + 1 =
48. 7 + 9 =
49. 9 + 9 =
50. 9 + 8 =

Addition Facts

Letter A, Day 1

Dear parents,

Our class is learning the addition facts. We are using a system which may be different than the way you learned your addition facts. You can help your child learn these facts by drilling the designated set of facts daily and reviewing previously learned facts. Please only drill the facts listed because the system works best when followed exactly.

The facts are grouped into seven day's work. Today we are memorizing the following. Please work with your child so he/she will be able to quickly and mentally answer the sums without counting on his/her fingers.

Today's problems

1 + 0 = 1	2 + 2 = 4	2 + 4 = 6
1 + 1 = 2	2 + 3 = 5	3 + 3 = 6
1 + 2 = 3	2 + 5 = 7	3 + 4 = 7

Thank you for assisting me,

....

Teacher

Extra notes ....

Addition Facts

Letter B, Day 2

Dear parents,

This is our second day of learning addition facts.

Please drill your child on these facts:

2 + 6 = 8	3 + 5 = 8	4 + 4 = 8
2 + 7 = 9	3 + 6 = 9	4 + 5 = 9

Review the following

1 + 0 = 1	2 + 2 = 4	3 + 3 = 6
1 + 1 = 2	2 + 3 = 5	2 + 5 = 7
1 + 2 = 3	2 + 4 = 6	3 + 4 = 7

Thank you for your help,

....

Teacher

Extra notes ....

Addition Facts

Dear parents,

Today we are learning the following addition facts.

Please help by drilling your child on these facts:

2 + 8 = 10	2 + 9 = 11
3 + 7 = 10	3 + 8 = 11
4 + 6 = 10	4 + 7 = 11
5 + 5 = 10	5 + 6 = 11

Review the following

1 + 0 = 1	2 + 4 = 6	3 + 5 = 8
1 + 1 = 2	3 + 3 = 6	4 + 4 = 8
1 + 2 = 3	2 + 5 = 7	2 + 7 = 9
2 + 2 = 4	3 + 4 = 7	3 + 6 = 9
2 + 3 = 5	2 + 6 = 8	4 + 5 = 9

Thank you for your help,

....

Teacher

Extra notes ....

...tion Facts

Letter D, Day 4

Dear parents,

This is our fourth day of learning all of the addition facts.

Please help your child memorize the following:

3 + 9 = 12	
4 + 8 = 12	4 + 9 = 13
5 + 7 = 12	5 + 8 = 13
6 + 6 = 12	6 + 7 = 13

Review the following

1 + 0 = 1	3 + 4 = 7	2 + 8 = 10
1 + 1 = 2	2 + 6 = 8	3 + 7 = 10
1 + 2 = 3	3 + 5 = 8	4 + 6 = 10
2 + 2 = 4	4 + 4 = 8	5 + 5 = 10
2 + 3 = 5	2 + 7 = 9	2 + 9 = 11
2 + 4 = 6	3 + 6 = 9	3 + 8 = 11
3 + 3 = 6	4 + 5 = 9	4 + 7 = 11
2 + 5 = 7		5 + 6 = 11

Thanks for your help,

....

Teacher

Extra notes ....

Addition Facts

Dear parents,

On this fifth day of our systematic process of learning all of the addition facts, we are asking your child to memorize this new set of facts.

Please drill your child on these facts:

5 + 9 = 14	7 + 7 = 14	6 + 9 = 15
6 + 8 = 14		7 + 8 = 15

Review the following

1 + 0 = 1	3 + 5 = 8	3 + 8 = 11
1 + 1 = 2	4 + 4 = 8	4 + 7 = 11
1 + 2 = 3	2 + 7 = 9	5 + 6 = 11
2 + 2 = 4	3 + 6 = 9	3 + 9 = 12
2 + 3 = 5	4 + 5 = 9	4 + 8 = 12
2 + 4 = 6	2 + 8 = 10	5 + 7 = 12
3 + 3 = 6	3 + 7 = 10	6 + 6 = 12
2 + 5 = 7	4 + 6 = 10	4 + 9 = 13
3 + 4 = 7	5 + 5 = 10	5 + 8 = 13
2 + 6 = 8	2 + 9 = 11	6 + 7 = 13

Thanks for your help,

....

Teacher

Extra notes ....

....

Addition Facts

Dear parents,

Today we will finish all of the addition facts we have been studying over the last six days.

Please help your child memorize this set of facts:

7 + 9 =16	8 + 8 =16	8 + 9 =17	9 + 9 = 18

Review the following

1 + 0 = 1	2 + 6 = 8	5 + 5 =10	4 + 9 = 13
1 + 1 = 2	3 + 5 = 8	2 + 9 =11	5 + 8 = 13
1 + 2 = 3	4 + 4 = 8	3 + 8 =11	6 + 7 = 13
2 + 2 = 4	2 + 7 = 9	4 + 7 =11	5 + 9 = 14
2 + 3 = 5	3 + 6 = 9	5 + 6 =11	6 + 8 = 14
2 + 4 = 6	4 + 5 = 9	3 + 9 =12	7 + 7 = 14
3 + 3 = 6	2 + 8 =10	4 + 8 =12	6 + 9 = 15
2 + 5 = 7	3 + 7 =10	5 + 7 =12	7 + 8 = 15
3 + 4 = 7	4 + 6 =10	6 + 6 =12	

Thank you for your help,

....

Teacher

Extra notes ....

....

....

....

Addition Facts

Tables

+	0	1	2	3	4	5	6	7	8	9
0	0	1	2	3	4	5	6	7	8	9
1	1	2	3	4	5	6	7	8	9	10
2	2	3	4	5	6	7	8	9	10	11
3	3	4	5	6	7	8	9	10	11	12
4	4	5	6	7	8	9	10	11	12	13
5	5	6	7	8	9	10	11	12	13	14
6	6	7	8	9	10	11	12	13	14	15
7	7	8	9	10	11	12	13	14	15	16
8	8	9	10	11	12	13	14	15	16	17
9	9	10	11	12	13	14	15	16	17	18

+	0	1	2	3	4	5	6	7	8	9
0	0	1	2	3	4	5	6	7	8	9
1	1	2	3	4	5	6	7	8	9	10
2	2	3	4	5	6	7	8	9	10	11
3	3	4	5	6	7	8	9	10	11	12
4	4	5	6	7	8	9	10	11	12	13
5	5	6	7	8	9	10	11	12	13	14
6	6	7	8	9	10	11	12	13	14	15
7	7	8	9	10	11	12	13	14	15	16
8	8	9	10	11	12	13	14	15	16	17
9	9	10	11	12	13	14	15	16	17	18

+	0	1	2	3	4	5	6	7	8	9
0	0	1	2	3	4	5	6	7	8	9
1	1	2	3	4	5	6	7	8	9	10
2	2	3	4	5	6	7	8	9	10	11
3	3	4	5	6	7	8	9	10	11	12
4	4	5	6	7	8	9	10	11	12	13
5	5	6	7	8	9	10	11	12	13	14
6	6	7	8	9	10	11	12	13	14	15
7	7	8	9	10	11	12	13	14	15	16
8	8	9	10	11	12	13	14	15	16	17
9	9	10	11	12	13	14	15	16	17	18

+	0	1	2	3	4	5	6	7	8	9
0	0	1	2	3	4	5	6	7	8	9
1	1	2	3	4	5	6	7	8	9	10
2	2	3	4	5	6	7	8	9	10	11
3	3	4	5	6	7	8	9	10	11	12
4	4	5	6	7	8	9	10	11	12	13
5	5	6	7	8	9	10	11	12	13	14
6	6	7	8	9	10	11	12	13	14	15
7	7	8	9	10	11	12	13	14	15	16
8	8	9	10	11	12	13	14	15	16	17
9	9	10	11	12	13	14	15	16	17	18

+	0	1	2	3	4	5	6	7	8	9
0	0	1	2	3	4	5	6	7	8	9
1	1	2	3	4	5	6	7	8	9	10
2	2	3	4	5	6	7	8	9	10	11
3	3	4	5	6	7	8	9	10	11	12
4	4	5	6	7	8	9	10	11	12	13
5	5	6	7	8	9	10	11	12	13	14
6	6	7	8	9	10	11	12	13	14	15
7	7	8	9	10	11	12	13	14	15	16
8	8	9	10	11	12	13	14	15	16	17
9	9	10	11	12	13	14	15	16	17	18

+	0	1	2	3	4	5	6	7	8	9
0	0	1	2	3	4	5	6	7	8	9
1	1	2	3	4	5	6	7	8	9	10
2	2	3	4	5	6	7	8	9	10	11
3	3	4	5	6	7	8	9	10	11	12
4	4	5	6	7	8	9	10	11	12	13
5	5	6	7	8	9	10	11	12	13	14
6	6	7	8	9	10	11	12	13	14	15
7	7	8	9	10	11	12	13	14	15	16
8	8	9	10	11	12	13	14	15	16	17
9	9	10	11	12	13	14	15	16	17	18

Answers

Tests

Test for Day 2 .... pg 13

1. 3 — 11. 4
2. 5 — 12. 3
3. 7 — 13. 5
4. 4 — 14. 4
5. 6 — 15. 5
6. 7 — 16. 6
7. 6 — 17. 7
8. 4 — 18. 5
9. 5 — 19. 7
10. 6 — 20. 6

Test for Day 3 .... pg 14

1. 9 — 13. 9
2. 4 — 14. 9
3. 7 — 15. 7
4. 9 — 16. 9
5. 5 — 17. 8
6. 9 — 18. 8
7. 8 — 19. 6
8. 9 — 20. 9
9. 6 — 21. 8
10. 8 — 22. 9
11. 9 — 23. 5
12. 8 — 24. 9

Test for Day 4 .... pg 15

1. 10 — 13. 9
2. 8 — 14. 5
3. 10 — 15. 11
4. 8 — 16. 11
5. 10 — 17. 8
6. 9 — 18. 10
7. 6 — 19. 11
8. 7 — 20. 9
9. 11 — 21. 11
10. 7 — 22. 6
11. 10 — 23. 6
12. 11 — 24. 10

Test for Day 5 .... pg 16

1. 8 — 14. 12
2. 10 — 15. 11
3. 12 — 16. 12
4. 10 — 17. 11
5. 13 — 18. 13
6. 13 — 19. 11
7. 11 — 20. 8
8. 9 — 21. 13
9. 11 — 22. 11
10. 12 — 23. 13
11. 9 — 24. 12
12. 13 — 25. 9
13. 8 — 26. 6

Test for Day 6 .... pg 17

1. 15 — 5. 15
2. 14 — 6. 12
3. 13 — 7. 11
4. 11 — 8. 15
9. 12 — 25. 9
10. 10 — 26. 15
11. 14 — 27. 13
12. 8 — 28. 12
13. 13 — 29. 10
14. 10 — 30. 14
15. 8 — 31. 11
16. 9 — 32. 14
17. 14 — 33. 12
18. 7 — 34. 12
19. 13 — 35. 10
20. 14 — 36. 15
21. 8 — 37. 8
22. 14 — 38. 11
23. 15 — 39. 16
24. 14 — 40. 6

Test for Day 7 .... pg 18

1. 18 — 26. 13
2. 15 — 27. 10
3. 8 — 28. 16
4. 13 — 29. 10
5. 11 — 30. 8
6. 8 — 31. 13
7. 15 — 32. 15
8. 15 — 33. 9
9. 13 — 34. 14
10. 14 — 35. 11
11. 9 — 36. 15
12. 7 — 37. 12
13. 16 — 38. 12
14. 11 — 39. 13
15. 12 — 40. 17
16. 14 — 41. 15
17. 14 — 42. 12
18. 12 — 43. 12
19. 16 — 44. 11
20. 13 — 45. 15
21. 10 — 46. 17
22. 3 — 47. 12
23. 6 — 48. 18
24. 14 — 49. 9
25. 12 — 50. 13

Final Tests

Final Test A .... pg 19

1. 4 — 19. 11
2. 5 — 20. 11
3. 6 — 21. 12
4. 7 — 22. 12
5. 6 — 23. 12
6. 7 — 24. 12
7. 8 — 25. 13
8. 8 — 26. 13
9. 8 — 27. 13
10. 9 — 28. 14
11. 9 — 29. 14
12. 9 — 30. 14
13. 10 — 31. 15
14. 10 — 32. 15
15. 10 — 33. 16
16. 10 — 34. 16
17. 11 — 35. 17
18. 11 — 36. 18

Final Test B.............. pg 20

1. 5 — 19. 11
2. 6 — 20. 11
3. 4 — 21. 12
4. 7 — 22. 12
5. 6 — 23. 12
6. 7 — 24. 12
7. 8 — 25. 13
8. 8 — 26. 13
9. 8 — 27. 13
10. 9 — 28. 14
11. 9 — 29. 14
12. 9 — 30. 14
13. 10 — 31. 15
14. 10 — 32. 15
15. 10 — 33. 16
16. 10 — 34. 16
17. 11 — 35. 17
18. 11 — 36. 18

Final Test C.............. pg 21

1. 5 — 19. 7
2. 13 — 20. 7
3. 10 — 21. 16
4. 13 — 22. 11
5. 6 — 23. 10
6. 15 — 24. 18
7. 11 — 25. 8
8. 14 — 26. 12
9. 17 — 27. 16
10. 6 — 28. 14
11. 8 — 29. 12
12. 10 — 30. 9
13. 12 — 31. 14
14. 8 — 32. 11
15. 15 — 33. 11
16. 11 — 34. 10
17. 4 — 35. 15
18. 13 — 36. 12

Final Test D .... pg 22

1. 4 — 22. 15
2. 9 — 23. 6
3. 9 — 24. 12
4. 7 — 25. 16
5. 9 — 26. 13
6. 8 — 27. 9
7. 11 — 28. 10
8. 7 — 29. 10
9. 11 — 30. 8
10. 3 — 31. 12
11. 12 — 32. 10
12. 9 — 33. 11
13. 10 — 34. 6
14. 5 — 35. 14
15. 11 — 36. 13
16. 5 — 37. 16
17. 13 — 38. 8
18. 10 — 39. 4
19. 14 — 40. 12
20. 7 — 41. 6
21. 15 — 42. 14
43. 6 — 47. 10
44. 13 — 48. 16
45. 15 — 49. 18
46. 17 — 50. 17